TAKE ME TO THE MOON!

STORY AND PICTURES BY
SAL MURDOCCA

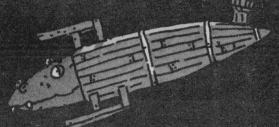

Published by
FIREFLY PAPERBACKS
A Scholastic Book Service

ALSO BY SAL MURDOCCA

The Boy Who Was A Raccoon

Tuttle's Shell

To my mother and Theresa

1 2 3 4 5 6 7 8 9 9 - 7 6 5 4 3 2 1 0 9
Printed in U.S.A.

ISBN 0-590-38338-8

CONTENTS

1
JUST DO IT!

"Take me to the moon!" said the Queen.

"But it's very far away," replied the Astrologer.

"I don't care," said the Queen. "Just do it!"

The Astrologer sighed and went to look at his star charts.

"Just as I expected," he said. "We're going to the moon."

The Astrologer ran to see the
Carpenter.

The Carpenter was taking a nap.
When the Astrologer knocked on
the door, the Carpenter shouted,
"Go away! I'm very busy!"
Then he put his pillow over his
head.

The Astrologer knocked again.
"It's no use," grumbled the
Carpenter.

He opened the door.

"What do you want?" he asked.

The Astrologer was out of breath.

"The Queen wants to go to the
moon!" he gasped. .

"Did you wake me up to tell me
that?" growled the Carpenter.

"Yes," the Astrologer said.
"You must build a rocket for
the trip."

"How can I do that?" shouted
the Carpenter.

"I really don't know," replied
the Astrologer. "Just do it!"

"Humph," the Carpenter
grumbled. "It's hard to take
a nap around here."

The next day he collected
the finest wood and the
strongest nails.

He worked day and night
for a month.

By the next full moon, a great
rocket stood outside the town.

"It's wonderful!" said the Astrologer.

"Can I take a nap now?" asked
the Carpenter.

"Just one moment," said the
Queen. "How does it fly?"

"Fly?" laughed the Carpenter.

"How can I make it fly?"

"JUST DO IT!" roared the Queen.

The Carpenter went to see
the Knight.

"We have a problem. The rocket
doesn't fly," said the Carpenter.

"I think it's nice just the way
it is," the Knight said cheerfully.

"The Queen says it has to fly,"
said the Carpenter.

"But how?" asked the Knight.

"I don't know," the Carpenter
snapped. "Just do it!"

Then he went home to take a nap.

The only thing the Knight knew
about was dragons.
So he decided to go out and
capture a dragon.
He climbed onto his horse.
"Let's go," he called out. "We're
off to capture a dragon!"
They galloped out to Dragon Park.
When they got there, the Knight
blew his hunting horn.
Then he covered his eyes and
counted to one hundred.
"Ready or not, here I come!"
he called.
Theresa the dragon loved to play
hide and seek with the Knight.

She hid behind a rock.

Then she called, "Here I am!"

The Knight listened carefully.

He rode toward the sound of

Theresa's voice.

Suddenly, Theresa jumped out

from behind the rock.

"BOO!" she shouted.

The horse was so scared that

he fainted.

The Knight fell to the ground.

He sounded like one hundred

tin cans falling.

"Are you all right?" asked Theresa.

"Yes," said the Knight, dusting

off his hunting horn.

"Then I'll go and hide again,"
said Theresa.

"You can't," the Knight said.

He tied a rope around her neck.

"Now that I've captured you, I'm

taking you back to the castle,"

he said.

"What for?" asked Theresa. "Are

you going to have me stuffed?"

"Of course not," smiled the Knight.

"You're going to help us take the

Queen to the moon."

"How?" asked Theresa.

"I don't know," replied the Knight.

"Just do it!"

2

READY FOR TAKE-OFF

The Knight led Theresa back to
the castle.

His horse followed behind them.

When the Carpenter saw Theresa,
he jumped out of bed.

"What am I supposed to do with
a dragon?" he shouted.

"Don't ask me," the Knight said.

"It was the only thing I could
think of."

"I see," said the Carpenter,
scratching his head.

Just then, the Queen and the
Astrologer came in.

"What are you going to do with
a dragon?" the Astrologer asked.

"I'm not sure," replied the
Carpenter. "I'll have to think
about it overnight."

"Overnight?" said the Queen.
"I won't have a dragon running
around here all night. Tie
her up!"

"I don't think Theresa will like
that," said the Knight.

A small cloud of smoke rose from
Theresa's nose.

"Who cares what she likes?" said
the Queen. "Just do it!"

This was too much for Theresa.

She lifted her head and roared
as loudly as she could.

She blew the roof right off

the Carpenter's workshop.

The Astrologer jumped into

the Queen's arms.

The Queen fell against the Knight.

The Knight tumbled to the ground

like one hundred tin cans falling.

The only one left standing was

the Carpenter.

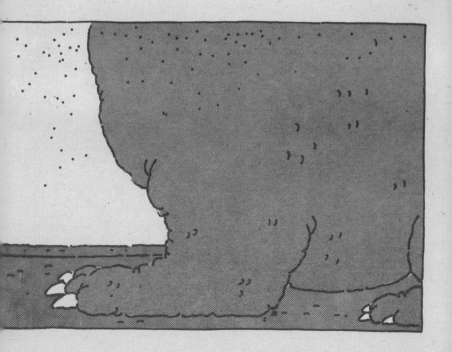

He watched the roof float back
onto his workshop.

He was smiling.

"What's so funny?" yelled the
Queen.

The Carpenter just kept smiling.

Now he knew how to make the
rocket fly.

By evening everything was ready
for take-off.

The Astrologer wanted to wait
until morning.

But the others said they wouldn't
be able to see the moon in the
daytime.

A grand parade marched up to

the rocket.

The band played and banners flew.

At the head of the parade was

the Queen.

Then came the Astrologer.

He had all his star charts.

Next came the Carpenter.

He had his pillow.

The Knight came last.

He was leading Theresa by

a long rope.

Theresa was very angry.

When they reached the rocket,

everyone climbed aboard.

Everyone but the Knight

and Theresa.

"Come on, Theresa," said the

Knight, tugging on the rope.

"All you have to do is back in

there."

He pointed to a space at the

rear of the rocket.

"I'm not moving one inch!" said

Theresa.

"What's going on down there?"

called the Queen.

"It's Theresa," the Knight called
back. "She won't move."

"Make her move!" shouted the
Queen. "I don't care how.
Just do it!"
The Knight looked at the crowd
of people around him.
"You heard the Queen. Now just
do it!" he said.
Everyone began to push Theresa
into the rear of the rocket.
They shoved, squeezed, tugged,
and poked to make her fit.
When she was in, Theresa shut
her eyes for a moment.
Then she opened them and said,
"I've had enough of this!"

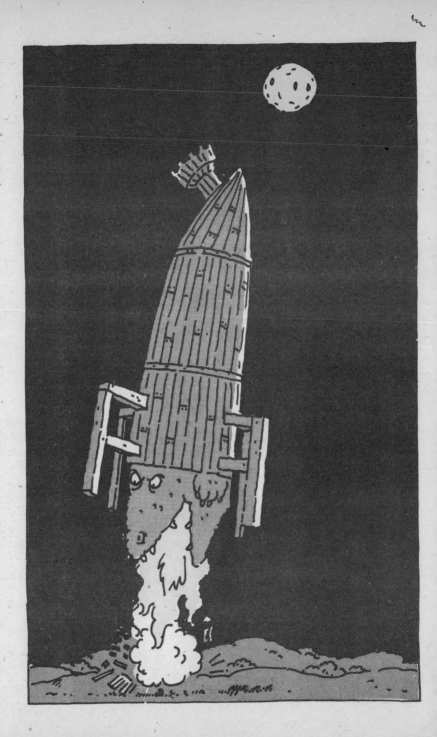

She blew a small puff of smoke.

The crowd started running.

The Knight quickly climbed
aboard the rocket.

The Queen asked the Carpenter,
"Are you sure this is going
to work?"

"Just hold on tight!" he replied.

Then Theresa began to roar.

Every hat in the crowd blew off.

The rocket lifted off and the
travelers were on their way.

3

ON THE MOON

The rocket zigzagged through
space at a very high speed.
Everyone held on for dear life.
"This is fun!" cried the Queen
as they whizzed along.
The Carpenter and the Knight
watched for shooting stars.
The Astrologer checked his star
charts.
After a while he looked up.

"Look!" he said. "There's the moon!"

"Tell Theresa to stop!" shouted the Queen.

"Tell Theresa to stop," said the Astrologer to the Carpenter.

"Tell Theresa to stop," said the Carpenter to the Knight.

"But she's very upset," the Knight said.

"Just do it!" said the others.

But just then Theresa saw the moon. She decided to make a landing.

She was getting tired.

"Thank goodness," the Knight said.

A few moments later the rocket
made a belly landing on the moon.
"OOF!" said Theresa.

Before the moon dust had time

to settle, everyone climbed out

of the rocket.

While they sneezed the moon

dust out of their noses,

Theresa squeezed herself out.

She lay on the moon and smoothed

out all of her rocket wrinkles.

She glared angrily at the others.

Then without a word, she rolled

over and went to sleep.

"What's she doing?" asked the

Queen.

"She's showing very good sense,"

the Carpenter said.

"She's very tired," said the Knight.

"So am I," said the Carpenter.

"Well, I'm not tired," the Queen
said. "I'm ready for a nice long
walk. I want to see the moon."

"Excuse me," said the Astrologer.
"I have to check my star charts."

"I think I'll take a nap," said
the Carpenter.

The Knight couldn't think of
an excuse not to go.
So he just said to the Queen,
"I hope you have a nice walk."

"We're all going for a walk,"
said the Queen. "It will be fun."

"But—" said the Astrologer.

"Just do it!" shouted the Queen.

They all walked for a long time.

They climbed over big rocks and

small rocks.

At last the Queen said, "There's

nothing to see but rocks!"

"I'm sleepy," the Carpenter said.

"So am I," said the Queen. "We're

going back to the rocket."

When they got back, Theresa was

still asleep.

"Lucky dragon!" grumbled the

Carpenter.

The Knight climbed up into the

rocket and got the sleeping bags.

Everyone settled down for a

good rest.

"Where's my pillow?" asked the

Queen.

No one knew what to say.

Somehow the Queen's pillow

had been left behind.

"The Carpenter has a pillow,"

said the Knight.

"Good!" said the Queen. "Give

it to me."

"But how can I sleep without it?"

the Carpenter asked.

"Just do it!" said the Queen.

"It's not fair," grumbled the

Carpenter.

But he soon fell asleep.

It had been a busy day.

WHERE'S THERESA?

Everyone slept for a long time.

When they woke up, they saw

the earth in the sky.

They began to feel homesick.

"I miss my horse," said the

Knight.

"I miss my own bed," said the

Carpenter.

"I miss my telescopes," said the

Astrologer.

"I miss everything," said the
Queen. "I want to go home!"
"I'm afraid we can't," the Knight
said.
"Why not?" snapped the Queen.
"Theresa's gone," replied the Knight.

"Gone?" said the Queen.

"GONE?" said the others.

"Where did she go?" asked the Queen.

"Maybe she found a better place to sleep," the Carpenter said.

"Then find her!" the Queen
shouted.

"Where shall we begin?" asked
the Astrologer.

"I don't care where," said the
Queen. "Just do it."

So the Astrologer, the Carpenter,
and the Knight went off to look
for Theresa.

The Queen stayed by the rocket
and sulked.

The others searched all over
the moon.

They climbed up and down hills.

They looked behind every rock.

At last they gave up and went
back to the rocket.

They were very tired.

"Well, where is she?" asked the
Queen.

"We couldn't find her," said the
Astrologer.

"We really tried," sighed the
Carpenter.

"We looked everywhere," said
the Knight. "I even blew my
hunting horn."

The Queen began to cry.

"I'm hungry and I want to go
home!" she sobbed.

"Please don't cry," said the
Astrologer.

"This is no fun!" cried the Queen.

Everyone felt the same way.

This was no fun.

They all sat down with the Queen
and began to cry, too.

Suddenly, above the sound of
sniffling, the Astrologer shouted,
"Look!"

There in the black sky, high
above their heads, floated
words made of smoke —
HELP HELP
HELP HELP

"Who wants help?" sniffled the
Carpenter.

"Theresa needs help!" cried the
Knight.

A cloud of moon dust rose
as everyone scrambled toward
the smoke signals.

"Wait for me!" called the Queen.

5

WE DID IT!

The Knight, the Carpenter, the
Astrologer, and the Queen
followed the smoke signals.
At last they came to a deep hole.
They knew it was deep, because
just at the edge of the hole
was the tip of Theresa's nose.
"Theresa!" said the Knight.
"Why are you playing hide
and seek?"

"She's not playing hide and seek," the Carpenter said. "Can't you see that she's found a good place to sleep?"

"I think she's found a good place to watch the stars," said the Astrologer.

"If you ask me," said the Queen, "she was looking for something to eat."

"It just so happens that all of you are wrong," said Theresa through her nose. "I was taking a walk. I didn't see this hole until I fell into it. Now I'm stuck."

"You sound very strange," the
Knight said.

"That's because I can't open
my mouth," Theresa mumbled.
"Pull her out," said the Queen.
"I want to go home, now!"
The Knight took hold of
Theresa's nose and pulled.
"Ouch!" said Theresa.
But she didn't budge.

The Knight looked at the Carpenter.

"Don't look at me," said the Carpenter. "I'm just the Carpenter."

"Just do it!" said the Knight.

The Carpenter took hold of Theresa's nose too.

"Ouch! Ouch!" said Theresa. But she didn't budge an inch.

The Carpenter looked at the Astrologer.

"Don't look at me!" said the Astrologer. "I'm just the Astrologer."

"Just do it!" said the Carpenter.

All three pulled on Theresa's nose.

"Ouch! Ouch! Ouch!" said Theresa.

But she still didn't move a bit.

They all looked at the Queen.

"Don't look at me!" said the Queen.

"I'm the Queen."

The Astrologer, the Carpenter, and

the Knight looked at one another.

Then they turned to the Queen

and said, "Just do it!"

All four began to pull on Theresa's

nose.

"That's four ouches!" said Theresa.

But this time she moved just
a little.

"Pull harder!" Theresa said.

"I can't!" cried the Queen.

"JUST DOOOO IT!" roared
Theresa.

She moved a little bit more.

They pulled and pulled until

at last Theresa popped out.

"We did it!" the Queen shouted.

Theresa shook herself.

"I'm hungry," she said. "Let's go home."

"Can you roar when you're not

angry?" asked the Knight.

"I always roar when I'm hungry,"

Theresa replied.

"Then let's go!" the Knight shouted.

Just before they took off, the
Queen said, "That was fun! It's
the first time I ever helped do
anything!"

"It was a good time to start,"
said Theresa.

She began to roar and the rocket
rose above the moon.

"Can I take my nap now?" asked
the Carpenter.